Find Us on Instagram
@prettyplannersnote
email us
prettyplannersnote@gmail.com

We love connecting with you!

WELCOME TO
THE
Shitshow

This JOURNAL
Belongs To

_____

Introduction

Sometimes, You Just Want To Cuss and Let the Steam Out. Welcome to The Shit Show Gratitude Journal. This Journal are for those Moment When You are feeling Low. Uplift Your Spirit and Soul with this Snarky, sassy and Hilarious Quotes While You sip on a good cup of coffee, the smell of rain, starting a good book - you begin each day on the right note.

Hope you Enjoy This Journal.

Thanks

Staci G.

Asshole of the Day

Date:__/__/__

Today, I'm Thankful For...

Today, I'm Happy I didn't... Today, I'm Proud I did...

My Mood Today (Rated in Strawberries)

Capture Random Shit Here

Other Shit To Remember...

Date:___/___/___

Asshole of the Day

Today, I'm Thankful For...

Today, I'm Happy I didn't...

Today, I'm Proud I did...

My Mood Today (Rated in Strawberries)

Capture Random Shit Here

I
Hate
Inspirational
Quotes

Other Shit To Remember...

Asshole of the Day

Today, I'm Thankful For...

Today, I'm Happy I didn't...

Today, I'm Proud I did...

My Mood Today (Rated in Strawberries)

Date:__/__/__

Asshole of the Day

Today, I'm Thankful For...

Today, I'm Happy I didn't...

Today, I'm Proud I did...

My Mood Today (Rated in Strawberries)

Capture Random Shit Here

GOEST &
FUCKETH
THYSELF

Other Shit To Remember...

Asshole of the Day

Today, I'm Thankful For...

Today, I'm Happy I didn't...

Today, I'm Proud I did...

My Mood Today (Rated in Strawberries)

Capture Random Shit Here

Other Shit To Remember...

Asshole of the Day

_____
_____
_____
_____
_____
_____
_____

Today, I'm Thankful For...

_____
_____
_____
_____
_____
_____
_____
_____

Today, I'm Happy I didn't...

_____
_____
_____
_____
_____

Today, I'm Proud I did...

_____
_____
_____
_____
_____

My Mood Today (Rated in Strawberries)

Capture Random Shit Here

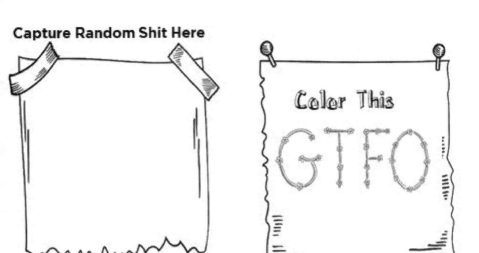

Color This

GTFO

Other Shit To Remember...

Asshole of the Day

_____
_____
_____
_____
_____
_____
_____

Today, I'm Thankful For...

_____
_____
_____
_____
_____
_____
_____

Today, I'm Happy I didn't...

_____
_____
_____
_____
_____

Today, I'm Proud I did...

_____
_____
_____
_____
_____

My Mood Today (Rated in Strawberries)

Hang Your Shit Here

IN LOVING MEMORY OF WHEN I GAVE A SHIT

Other Shit To Remember...

🍓 Asshole of the Day

_____
_____
_____
_____
_____
_____
_____
_____

🍓 Today, I'm Thankful For...

_____
_____
_____
_____
_____
_____
_____
_____

Today, I'm Happy I didn't... 🍓 Today, I'm Proud I did...

_____	_____
_____	_____
_____	_____
_____	_____

My Mood Today (Rated in Strawberries)

🍓 🍓 🍓 🍓 🍓 🍓 🍓 🍓 🍓 🍓 🍓

Capture Random Shit Here

"Everyone seems normal until you get to know them."

Other Shit To Remember...

Date:__/__/__

Asshole of the Day

Today, I'm Thankful For...

Today, I'm Happy I didn't...

Today, I'm Proud I did...

My Mood Today (Rated in Strawberries)

Capture Random Shit Here

I'M A
CLASSY
MOTHER
FUCKER

Other Shit To Remember...

Asshole of the Day

Today, I'm Thankful For...

Today, I'm Happy I didn't...

Today, I'm Proud I did...

My Mood Today (Rated in Strawberries)

Capture Random Shit Here

And in That
Moment, I
Swear I Still
didn't give
A Shit

Other Shit To Remember...

Date:__/__/__

Asshole of the Day

Today, I'm Thankful For...

Today, I'm Happy I didn't...

Today, I'm Proud I did...

My Mood Today (Rated in Strawberries)

Hang Your Shit Here

Do More of What Makes You Happy. Fuck Everything Else.

Other Shit To Remember...

Date:___/___/___

Asshole of the Day

Today, I'm Thankful For...

Today, I'm Happy I didn't... Today, I'm Proud I did...

My Mood Today (Rated in Strawberries)

Capture Random Shit Here

THERE
IS ALWAYS
something
TO BE
grateful
for

Other Shit To Remember...

🍓 Asshole of the Day

_____
_____
_____
_____
_____
_____
_____
_____

🍓 Today, I'm Thankful For...

_____
_____
_____
_____
_____
_____
_____
_____

Today, I'm Happy I didn't... 🍓 Today, I'm Proud I did...

_____	_____
_____	_____
_____	_____
_____	_____
_____	_____

My Mood Today (Rated in Strawberries)

🍓 🍓 🍓 🍓 🍓 🍓 🍓 🍓 🍓 🍓 🍓

Capture Random Shit Here

Askhole:

- A Person who constantly asks for advice, yet Always does the opposite of what you told them.

Other Shit To Remember...

Date:__/__/__

Asshole of the Day

Today, I'm Thankful For...

Today, I'm Happy I didn't...

Today, I'm Proud I did...

My Mood Today (Rated in Strawberries)

Capture Random Shit Here

FUCK

- VERB [FAAK]
· ing · er · s

Fuck can be used in many ways and is probably the only fucking word that can be put every fuckingwhere and still make fucking sense. Fuckers

Other Shit To Remember...

Date:__/__/__

Asshole of the Day

(lined writing area)

Today, I'm Thankful For...

(lined writing area)

Today, I'm Happy I didn't...

(lined writing area)

Today, I'm Proud I did...

(lined writing area)

My Mood Today (Rated in Strawberries)

Date:__/__/__

Asshole of the Day

Today, I'm Thankful For...

Today, I'm Happy I didn't...

Today, I'm Proud I did...

My Mood Today (Rated in Strawberries)

Capture Random Shit Here

STRAIGHT OUTTA FUCK OFF

Other Shit To Remember...

Date:___/___/___

🍓 Asshole of the Day

🍓 Today, I'm Thankful For...

Today, I'm Happy I didn't...   🍓   Today, I'm Proud I did...

My Mood Today (Rated in Strawberries)

🍓 🍓 🍓 🍓 🍓 🍓 🍓 🍓 🍓 🍓 🍓

Capture Random Shit Here

I'M HERE TO FUCK SHIT UP

Other Shit To Remember...

Date:___/___/___

Asshole of the Day

Today, I'm Thankful For...

Today, I'm Happy I didn't...

Today, I'm Proud I did...

My Mood Today (Rated in Strawberries)

Capture Random Shit Here

THE KEY TO
HAPPINESS
IS TO STOP
GIVING A
FUCK.

Other Shit To Remember...

Asshole of the Day

Today, I'm Thankful For...

Today, I'm Happy I didn't...

Today, I'm Proud I did...

My Mood Today (Rated in Strawberries)

Hang Your Shit Here

Other Shit To Remember...

Date:___/___/___

Asshole of the Day

🍓 Today, I'm Thankful For...

Today, I'm Happy I didn't...   🍓   Today, I'm Proud I did...

My Mood Today (Rated in Strawberries)

🍓 🍓 🍓 🍓 🍓 🍓 🍓 🍓 🍓 🍓 🍓

BE THE
REASON
SOMEONE
SMILES
TODAY.

Capture Random Shit Here

Other Shit To Remember...

Date:___/___/___

Asshole of the Day

Today, I'm Thankful For...

Today, I'm Happy I didn't...   Today, I'm Proud I did...

My Mood Today (Rated in Strawberries)

Capture Random Shit Here

I DON'T HAVE THE ENERGY TO PRETEND TO LIKE YOU TODAY

Other Shit To Remember...

Asshole of the Day

Today, I'm Thankful For...

Today, I'm Happy I didn't...

Today, I'm Proud I did...

My Mood Today (Rated in Strawberries)

Capture Random Shit Here

"hey! fear! its me! GO FUCK YOURSELF! Sincerely, Me"

Other Shit To Remember...

Date:___/___/___

Asshole of the Day

_____
_____
_____
_____
_____
_____
_____

Today, I'm Thankful For...

_____
_____
_____
_____
_____
_____
_____

Today, I'm Happy I didn't...

_____
_____
_____
_____
_____

Today, I'm Proud I did...

_____
_____
_____
_____
_____

My Mood Today (Rated in Strawberries)

Asshole of the Day

_____

Today, I'm Thankful For...

_____

Today, I'm Happy I didn't...

Today, I'm Proud I did...

My Mood Today (Rated in Strawberries)

Deja Poo

adj. The Feeling of having heard this crap before.

Capture Random Shit Here

Other Shit To Remember...

Date:__/__/__

Asshole of the Day

Today, I'm Thankful For...

Today, I'm Happy I didn't...

Today, I'm Proud I did...

My Mood Today (Rated in Strawberries)

Capture Random Shit Here

DEJA MOO

when you
know you
have
experienced
this **BULLSHIT**
Before

Other Shit To Remember...

Asshole of the Day Date:__/__/__

Today, I'm Thankful For...

Today, I'm Happy I didn't...   **Today, I'm Proud I did...**

My Mood Today (Rated in Strawberries)

Capture Random Shit Here

Its Beginning to Look a lot Like Fuck This.

Other Shit To Remember...

Asshole of the Day

Today, I'm Thankful For...

Today, I'm Happy I didn't...

Today, I'm Proud I did...

My Mood Today (Rated in Strawberries)

Hang Your Shit Here

"Always remember that you're unique. Just like everyone else."

Other Shit To Remember...

Date:__/__/__

Asshole of the Day

Today, I'm Thankful For...

Today, I'm Happy I didn't...

Today, I'm Proud I did...

My Mood Today (Rated in Strawberries)

Fuck You You Fucking Fuck!

Capture Random Shit Here

Other Shit To Remember...

Date:___/___/___

Asshole of the Day

Today, I'm Thankful For...

Today, I'm Happy I didn't...

Today, I'm Proud I did...

My Mood Today (Rated in Strawberries)

Capture Random Shit Here

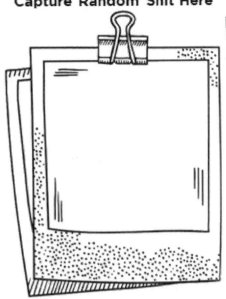

SORRY I'M LATE I DIDN'T WANT TO COME

Other Shit To Remember...

Date:___/___/___

Asshole of the Day

Today, I'm Thankful For...

Today, I'm Happy I didn't...

Today, I'm Proud I did...

My Mood Today (Rated in Strawberries)

Capture Random Shit Here

"Silence is golden. Duct tape is silver."

Other Shit To Remember...

Date:___/___/___

Asshole of the Day

Today, I'm Thankful For...

Today, I'm Happy I didn't...

Today, I'm Proud I did...

My Mood Today (Rated in Strawberries)

Hang Your Shit Here

"No, you don't have to repeat yourself. I was ignoring you the first time."

Other Shit To Remember...

Asshole of the Day

Today, I'm Thankful For...

Today, I'm Happy I didn't... Today, I'm Proud I did...

My Mood Today (Rated in Strawberries)

Capture Random Shit Here

I LOVE THE SOUND YOU MAKE WHEN YOU SHUT UP

Other Shit To Remember...

Date:___/___/___

Asshole of the Day

Today, I'm Thankful For...

Today, I'm Happy I didn't...

Today, I'm Proud I did...

My Mood Today (Rated in Strawberries)

Capture Random Shit Here

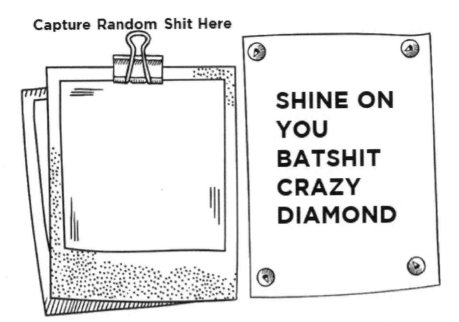

SHINE ON
YOU
BATSHIT
CRAZY
DIAMOND

Other Shit To Remember...

Date:___/___/___

Asshole of the Day

🍓 Today, I'm Thankful For...

Today, I'm Happy I didn't... 🍓 Today, I'm Proud I did...

My Mood Today (Rated in Strawberries)

Capture Random Shit Here

SWEAT DRIES
BLOOD CLOTS
BONE HEALS

SUCK IT UP
PRINCESS

Other Shit To Remember...

Date:___/___/___

Asshole of the Day

Today, I'm Thankful For...

Today, I'm Happy I didn't...   Today, I'm Proud I did...

My Mood Today (Rated in Strawberries)

Hang Your Shit Here

LETS KEEP -THE- DUMBFUCKERY TO A MINIMUM TODAY.

Other Shit To Remember...

Date:__/__/__

Asshole of the Day

Today, I'm Thankful For...

Today, I'm Happy I didn't...

Today, I'm Proud I did...

My Mood Today (Rated in Strawberries)

Capture Random Shit Here

I WON'T
QUIT
BUT I WILL
CUSS
THE WHOLE TIME

Other Shit To Remember...

Date:___/___/___

Asshole of the Day

Today, I'm Thankful For...

Today, I'm Happy I didn't...

Today, I'm Proud I did...

My Mood Today (Rated in Strawberries)

Capture Random Shit Here

OH DEAR,
I SEEMED
TO HAVE
MISPLACED
THAT RAT
ASS I WAS
GOING TO
GIVE.

Other Shit To Remember...

Date:___/___/___

Asshole of the Day

Today, I'm Thankful For...

Today, I'm Happy I didn't...

Today, I'm Proud I did...

My Mood Today (Rated in Strawberries)

Capture Random Shit Here

LIFE IS
TOUGH
MY
DARLING
BUT SO
ARE YOU

Other Shit To Remember...

Date:___/___/___

Asshole of the Day

Today, I'm Thankful For...

Today, I'm Happy I didn't...

Today, I'm Proud I did...

My Mood Today (Rated in Strawberries)

Hang Your Shit Here

"GROW THROUGH WHAT YOU GO THROUGH"

Other Shit To Remember...

Date:___/___/___

Asshole of the Day

Today, I'm Thankful For...

Today, I'm Happy I didn't...

Today, I'm Proud I did...

My Mood Today (Rated in Strawberries)

Capture Random Shit Here

"JUST KEEP TALKING, I YAWN WHEN I'M INTERESTED."

Other Shit To Remember...

Date:__/__/__

Asshole of the Day

Today, I'm Thankful For...

Today, I'm Happy I didn't...

Today, I'm Proud I did...

My Mood Today (Rated in Strawberries)

Capture Random Shit Here

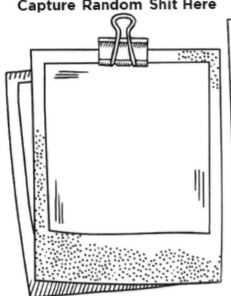

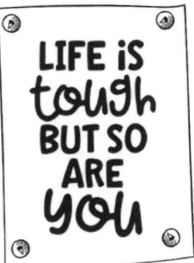

LIFE iS
tough
BUT SO
ARE
you

Other Shit To Remember...

Asshole of the Day

Date:___/___/___

Today, I'm Thankful For...

Today, I'm Happy I didn't...

Today, I'm Proud I did...

My Mood Today (Rated in Strawberries)

Capture Random Shit Here

PEOPLE ARE
ASSHOLES.
JUST MAKE
SURE YOU'RE
NOT THE
TOILET
PAPER

Other Shit To Remember...

Date:___/___/___

Asshole of the Day

Today, I'm Thankful For...

Today, I'm Happy I didn't...

Today, I'm Proud I did...

My Mood Today (Rated in Strawberries)

Date:___/___/___

Asshole of the Day

Today, I'm Thankful For...

Today, I'm Happy I didn't... Today, I'm Proud I did...

My Mood Today (Rated in Strawberries)

Capture Random Shit Here

I'M A NICE PERSON JUST DON'T PUSH THE BITCH BUTTON

Other Shit To Remember...

Date:__/__/__

Asshole of the Day

Today, I'm Thankful For...

Today, I'm Happy I didn't...

Today, I'm Proud I did...

My Mood Today (Rated in Strawberries)

Capture Random Shit Here

BE A
UNICORN
NOT A

TWATOPOTAMUS

Other Shit To Remember...

Asshole of the Day

Date:__/__/__

Today, I'm Thankful For...

Today, I'm Happy I didn't...

Today, I'm Proud I did...

My Mood Today (Rated in Strawberries)

Capture Random Shit Here

ONWARD BUTTERCUP, THERE'S **FUCKERY** TO SPREAD.

Other Shit To Remember...

Date:___/___/___

Asshole of the Day

Today, I'm Thankful For...

Today, I'm Happy I didn't...

Today, I'm Proud I did...

My Mood Today (Rated in Strawberries)

Hang Your Shit Here

I ROLLED MY EYES SO HARD, I CHECKED OUT MY OWN ASS

Other Shit To Remember...

Date:___/___/___

Asshole of the Day

Today, I'm Thankful For...

Today, I'm Happy I didn't...

Today, I'm Proud I did...

My Mood Today (Rated in Strawberries)

Capture Random Shit Here

THIS IS YOUR
WORLD.
SHAPE IT OR
SOMEONE
ELSE WILL.

Other Shit To Remember...

Date:___/___/___

Asshole of the Day

Today, I'm Thankful For...

Today, I'm Happy I didn't...

Today, I'm Proud I did...

My Mood Today (Rated in Strawberries)

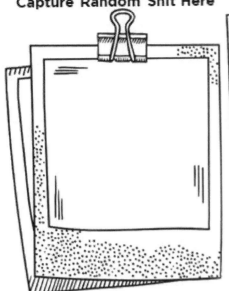

I DON'T
HAVE A
BUCKET
LIST BUT
MY FUCKET
LIST IS A
MILE LONG.

Other Shit To Remember...

Date:__/__/__

Asshole of the Day

Today, I'm Thankful For...

Today, I'm Happy I didn't...

Today, I'm Proud I did...

My Mood Today (Rated in Strawberries)

Capture Random Shit Here

IT'S ALL
SHITS AND
GIGGLES
UNTIL
SOMEONE
GIGGLES
AND SHITS.

Other Shit To Remember...

Date:___/___/___

Asshole of the Day

Today, I'm Thankful For...

Today, I'm Happy I didn't...   Today, I'm Proud I did...

My Mood Today (Rated in Strawberries)

Hang Your Shit Here

THROW ME TO THE WOLVES AND I'LL COME BACK LEADING THE PACK.

Other Shit To Remember...

Date:___/___/___

Asshole of the Day

🍓 Today, I'm Thankful For...

Today, I'm Happy I didn't... 🍓 Today, I'm Proud I did...

My Mood Today (Rated in Strawberries)

IF YOU ARE GOING TO RIDE MY ASS. YOU COULD AT LEAST PULL MY HAIR

Capture Random Shit Here

Other Shit To Remember...

Today's Shit List
PEOPLE, PLACE OR THINGS

- [ ] _____
- [ ] _____
- [ ] _____
- [ ] _____
- [ ] _____
- [ ] _____
- [ ] _____
- [ ] _____
- [ ] _____
- [ ] _____
- [ ] _____
- [ ] _____
- [ ] _____
- [ ] _____
- [ ] _____
- [ ] _____
- [ ] _____
- [ ] _____

Today's Shit List

PEOPLE, PLACE OR THINGS

- [ ] _____
- [ ] _____
- [ ] _____
- [ ] _____
- [ ] _____
- [ ] _____
- [ ] _____
- [ ] _____
- [ ] _____
- [ ] _____
- [ ] _____
- [ ] _____
- [ ] _____
- [ ] _____
- [ ] _____
- [ ] _____
- [ ] _____

Thank You

If you enjoyed this Beautiful and Sassy Journal, please take a little time to share your thoughts and post a Review on Amazon. To help customers Looking to buy, and also to encourage me and make me serve you better. Thanks

We'll never be perfect, but that won't stop us from trying. Your feedback makes us serve you better. Send ideas, criticism, Compliment or anything else you think we should hear to >>

bookspaddy@gmail.com. We'll Reply you As soon as we receive your Mail. :)

Visit Our Author Page >> **STACI GIRON** For More Amazing Books For Kids and Grown-Ups

Made in the USA
Columbia, SC
02 October 2020